Independent Schools
Examinations Board

MATHEMATICS
QUESTIONS AT 11+
(YEAR 6)

Book B:
Answer Book

compiled by
David E Hanson

Independent Schools
Examinations Board

www.galorepark.co.uk

GALORE PARK

Published by ISEB Publications, an imprint of Galore Park Publishing
19/21 Sayers Lane, Tenterden, Kent TN30 6BW
www.galorepark.co.uk

Printed and bound in the UK by Charlesworth Press, Wakefield

ISBN: 978 1 907047 14 5

First published 2006, reprinted 2009, 2011, 2012, 2013

Details of other ISEB publications and examination papers, and Galore Park
publications are available at www.galorepark.co.uk

CONTENTS

page

STRAND 4: ALGEBRA (PRE-ALGEBRA)

A Equations and formulae 1
B Sequences and functions 10
C Graphs 13

STRAND 5: SHAPE, SPACE AND MEASURES

A Measures 22
B Shape 38
C Space 54

STRAND 6: HANDLING DATA

A Data handling 78
B Probability 104

NOTES

For each question the **Mark** is suggested as being appropriate, but teachers may wish to make adjustments depending on the age, ability and experience of pupils.

The **Additional Guidance** has been kept to a minimum to save excessive repetition. The following general guidelines may be helpful.

- Where no working is expected, the suggested mark reflects the difficulty of a question or the time it is likely to take. It is recommended that all or nothing should be awarded.

- Where the suggested mark covers a number of parts in a question, usually one mark will be awarded to each part except where indicated.

- Where working is asked for, or may reasonably be expected, all but one mark may be awarded for working showing method and / or understanding even if the answer is incorrect. Teachers will probably wish to award a reduced mark for a correct answer with no working.

- In the case of open-ended questions, it is recommended that full marks be awarded to a pupil who gives as many answers as may reasonably be expected in the time allowed. There is perhaps a good opportunity here for some differentiation according to pupil abilities.

- Where answers involve drawing, the suggested mark usually allows flexibility to take into account care and neatness.

- Where answers involve accurate drawing, the accuracy can generally be judged from measurements recorded later in the question.

- Where measurements are recorded, it is suggested that, for the questions in this book, full marks are generally awarded for

  (a) angle measurements which are up to two degrees out

  (b) length measurements which are up to two millimetres out.

It should be noted that, where drawn answers are given in this answer book, they are generally drawn to a slightly reduced scale, due to limitations of space.

STRAND 4: ALGEBRA (PRE-ALGEBRA)

A Equations and formulae

Q.	Answer	Mark	Additional Guidance
1. (i)	2 + 7 = 9	2	
(ii)	4 + 5 = 9	2	
(iii)	●●●●● and ●●●●●● is the same as ●●●●●●●●●●●	2	
(iv)	●●●●●● and ●●●● is the same as ●●●●●●●●●●	2	
2. (i)	6 − 4 = 2	2	
(ii)	8 − 3 = 5	2	
(iii)	8 − 7 = 1	2	
(iv)	taking ●●●●● from ●●●●●●●● leaves ●●●	2	
(v)	taking ●●● from ●●●●●●●●● leaves ●●●●●●	2	
(vi)	taking ●●●●●●●● from ●●●●●●●●●●●●●● leaves ●●●●●●	2	
3. (i)	2 × 6 = 12	2	
(ii)	2 × 8 = 16	2	
(iii)	3 × 6 = 18	2	
(iv)	● ● ● ● ● / ● ● ● ● ● is the same as ●●●●● / ●●●●●	2	

Q.	Answer	Mark	Additional Guidance
(v)	is the same as 	2	
4. (i)	8 ÷ 4 = 2	2	
(ii)	12 ÷ 2 = 6	2	
(iii)	gives 	2	
(iv)	gives 	2	
5. (i)	$\begin{aligned} 3 + 15 &= \textbf{18} \\ 15 + \textbf{3}\ &= 18 \end{aligned}$ $\begin{aligned} 18 - 15 &= \textbf{3} \\ \textbf{18} - 3\ &= 15 \end{aligned}$	2	
(ii)	$\begin{aligned} 4 + \textbf{7}\ &= \textbf{11} \\ \textbf{7} + \textbf{4}\ &= \textbf{11} \end{aligned}$ $\begin{aligned} \textbf{11} - 7\ &= \textbf{4} \\ \textbf{11} - \textbf{4}\ &= \textbf{7} \end{aligned}$	2	

6.	*examples:* 5 + 9 = 14
	              14 − 9 = 5
	
	or: 9 + 5 = 14
	             14 − 5 = 9
		1
		1	

7.	*examples:* 6 + 7 = 13
	              13 − 7 = 6
	
	or: 7 + 6 = 13
	             13 − 6 = 7
		1
		1	

ALGEBRA A

Q.	Answer	Mark	Additional Guidance
8. (i)	$6 \times 7 = \mathbf{42}$ $42 \div 6 = \mathbf{7}$ $7 \times \mathbf{6} = 42$ $42 \div \mathbf{7} = 6$	2	
(ii)	$\mathbf{7} \times 9 = \mathbf{63}$ $\mathbf{63} \div 9 = \mathbf{7}$ $\mathbf{9} \times 7 = \mathbf{63}$ $\mathbf{63} \div \mathbf{7} = \mathbf{9}$	4	
9. (i)	*examples:* $5 + 9 = 14$ and $14 - 9 = 5$ *or* $9 + 5 = 14$ and $14 - 5 = 9$	2	
(ii)	*examples:* $4 \times 9 = 36$ and $36 \div 4 = 9$ *or* $9 \times 4 = 36$ and $36 \div 9 = 4$	2	
10. (i)	cost = 5×10	1	
(ii)(a)	cost = $6 \times$?	1	
(b)	cost = number $\times$?	2	
(iii)	*example:* $c = n \times p$ use letters or symbols instead of words (c is cost, n is number, p is price)	2	
11. (i)	area = length $\times$ width	2	
(ii)	perimeter = $2 \times$ (length + width)	2	
12.	perimeter = $3 \times \ell$ (or 3ℓ)	2	
13. (i)	8	1	
(ii)	20 pence	1	
14.	6 cm	2	
15. (i)	$7 + 6 = \mathbf{13}$	1	
(ii)	$\mathbf{9} + 8 = 17$	1	
(iii)	$13 - 5 = \mathbf{8}$	1	
(iv)	$\mathbf{22} - 7 = 15$	1	

ALGEBRA A

Q.	Answer	Mark	Additional Guidance
16. (i)	3 × 8 = **24**	**1**	
(ii)	7 × **8** = 56	**1**	
(iii)	72 ÷ 9 = **8**	**1**	
(iv)	36 ÷ **4** = 9	**1**	
17. (i)	3 + 9 = **7** + 5	**1**	
(ii)	21 − 4 = 7 + **10**	**1**	
(iii)	24 ÷ 4 = 2 × **3**	**1**	
(iv)	**21** ÷ 3 = 3 + 4	**1**	
18.	23 + 12 = [**7**] × 5	**2**	
19.	5	**4**	
20. (i)	7	**1**	
(ii)	20	**1**	
(iii)	7	**1**	
(iv)	4	**2**	
21.	7	**1**	
22. (i)	5	**1**	
(ii)	15	**1**	
(iii)	2	**1**	
(iv)	5	**1**	
23. (i)	$40 - f = 19$ *or* $f + 19 = 40$	**2**	
(ii)	21	**1**	
24. (i)	$r + 13 = 32$	**2**	
(ii)	19	**1**	

ALGEBRA A

Q.	Answer	Mark	Additional Guidance
25. (i)	20	**1**	
(ii)	9	**2**	
26. (i)	1	**1**	
(ii)	⁻1	**2**	
(iii)	10	**1**	
27.	3 ⟶ **7** **0** ⟶ 4	**2**	
28.	2 ⟶ **7** 5 ⟶ **13** **9** ⟶ 21	**3**	
29.		**2**	
30.		**2**	
31.		**3**	

Q.	Answer		Mark	Additional Guidance
32.	$1\frac{1}{2}$ is the same as $\frac{3}{2}$		**2**	or suitable alternative
33. (i)	17		**1**	
(ii)	10		**1**	
(iii)	$2\frac{1}{2}$		**2**	
(iv)	⁻3		**1**	
34.	3 ⟶	**17**	**1**	
	0 ⟶	**2**	**1**	
	1 ⟶	7	**2**	
	4 ⟶	22	**2**	
35.	3 ⟶	**6**	**1**	
	27 ⟶	14	**2**	
	0 ⟶	5	**2**	
36. (i)	0 ⟶	**5**	**2**	
	4 ⟶	**17**		
(ii)	**12** ⟶	9	**2**	
	2 ⟶	4		
37.	12 ⟶	**11**	**1**	
	8 ⟶	9	**2**	
	10 ⟶	10	**2**	
38.	10 ⟶	**17**	**1**	
	6 ⟶	**9**	**1**	
	3 ⟶	**3**	**1**	
39. (i)	3 ⟶	**21**	**1**	
	0 ⟶	**12**	**1**	
	2 ⟶	18	**2**	

Q.	Answer	Mark	Additional Guidance
(ii)	*example:* input → ÷2 +5 → output *or* input → +10 ÷2 → output	3	
40.	7	2	
41.		3	
42.	9	2	
43. (i)	4	2	
(ii)	14	3	
44.	7	3	
45.	13	3	
46. (i)	25	1	
(ii)	12	2	
(iii)	48	2	
47. (i)	10	2	
(ii)	5 ⟶ 7 3 ⟶ 3	2	

ALGEBRA A

Q.	Answer	Mark	Additional Guidance
48. (i)	multiply every input number by 2	2	
(ii)(a)	− 5	1	
(b)	÷ 4	1	
49. (i)	6 12 18 24	3	any multiples of 6
(ii)	all are multiples of 6	2	
50.	12	2	

51.	John Janet
	  1 6
	  2 5
	  3 4
	  4 3
	  5 2
	  6 1
		3	

52.	6 and 4	2	
53.	16	3	numbers are 12 and 4
54.	Mary has 30p George has 20p	3	
55.	12 years	2	Ben is 8

Q.	Answer	Mark	Additional Guidance
56.	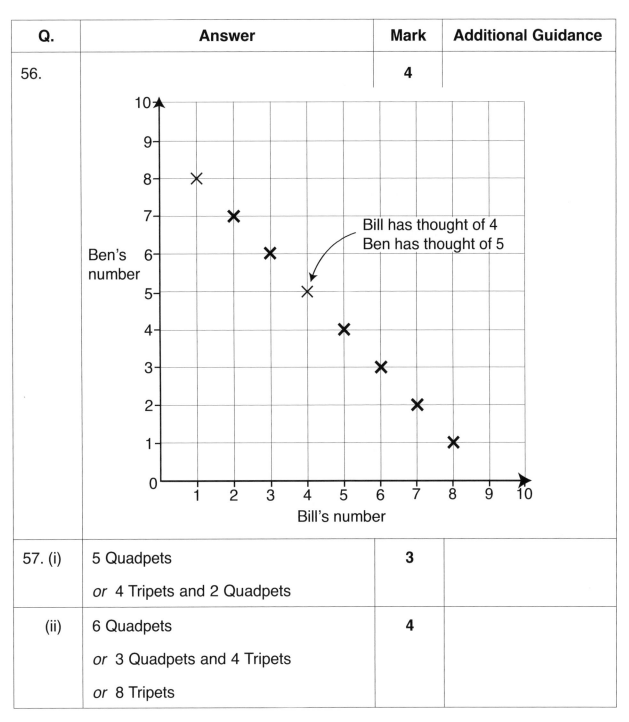	4	
57. (i)	5 Quadpets *or* 4 Tripets and 2 Quadpets	3	
(ii)	6 Quadpets *or* 3 Quadpets and 4 Tripets *or* 8 Tripets	4	

ALGEBRA A

B Sequences and functions

Q.	Answer	Mark	Additional Guidance
1.		**2**	
2.	1 2 **2** 1 2 2 1 **2** 2 **1** **2** **2**	**2**	
3. (i)	1, 3, 5, 7, 9, **11, 13**	**1**	
(ii)	1, 4, 7, 10, 13, **16, 19**	**2**	
(iii)	20, 18, 16, 14, 12, **10, 8**	**2**	
(iv)	$\frac{1}{2}$, 1, $1\frac{1}{2}$, 2, $2\frac{1}{2}$, **3, $3\frac{1}{2}$**	**2**	
4.	1, 4, 3, 6, 5, **8, 7**	**2**	
5. (i)	2 $\longrightarrow$ **4** 3 $\longrightarrow$ **6** 4 $\longrightarrow$ **8** 5 $\longrightarrow$ **10** 6 $\longrightarrow$ **12** 7 $\longrightarrow$ **14** 8 $\longrightarrow$ **16** 9 $\longrightarrow$ **18**	**2**	
(ii)	2	**1**	
6. (i)	× 7	**1**	
(ii)	*example:* **5** $\longrightarrow$ **35** **8** $\longrightarrow$ **56**	**2**	
7.	× 3	**2**	
8.	× 5	**2**	

Q.	Answer	Mark	Additional Guidance
9. (i)	*see below*	3	
(ii)		3	

(0)	1	2	(3)	4	5	(6)	7	8	(9)	10	11
(12)	13	14	(15)	16	17	(18)	19	20	(21)	22	23
(24)	25	26	(27)	28	29	(30)	31	32	(33)	34	35
(36)	37	38	(39)	40	41	(42)	43	44	(45)	46	47
(48)	49	50	(51)	52	53	(54)	55	56	(57)	58	59
(60)	61	62	(63)	64	65	(66)	67	68	(69)	70	71
(72)	73	74	(75)	76	77	(78)	79	80	(81)	82	83
(84)	85	86	(87)	88	89	(90)	91	92	(93)	94	95

Q.	Answer	Mark	Additional Guidance
10. (i)	*see below*	3	
(ii)		3	

(0)	1	2	3	(4)	5	6	7
(8)	9	10	11	(12)	13	14	15
(16)	17	18	19	(20)	21	22	23
(24)	25	26	27	(28)	29	30	31
(32)	33	34	35	(36)	37	38	39
(40)	41	42	43	(44)	45	46	47
(48)	49	50	51	(52)	53	54	55

ALGEBRA B

11

Q.	Answer	Mark	Additional Guidance
11.	**8** ————→———— 72 × 6 × 4 **24** ————→———— 72	**4**	

C Graphs

Q.	Answer	Mark	Additional Guidance
1. (i)	3 ⟶ 6 6 ⟶ 9	2	
(ii)		2	

ALGEBRA
C

Q.	Answer	Mark	Additional Guidance
2. (i)	4 ⟶ **12** 0 ⟶ **0**	**2**	
(ii)	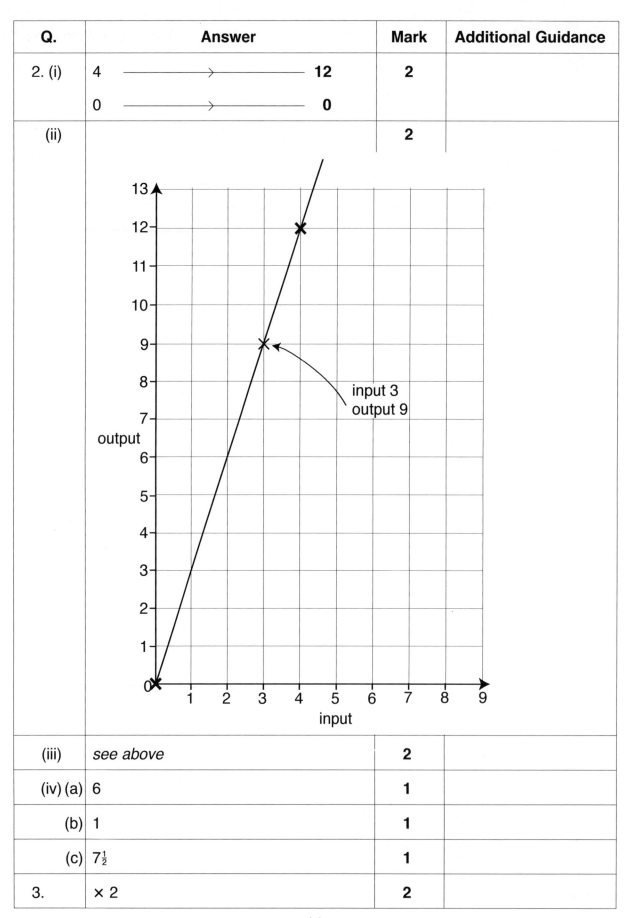	**2**	
(iii)	*see above*	**2**	
(iv) (a)	6	**1**	
(b)	1	**1**	
(c)	$7\frac{1}{2}$	**1**	
3.	× 2	**2**	

Q.	Answer	Mark	Additional Guidance
4. (i)	6	1	
(ii)	5	1	
(iii)	output = input plus one	2	
(iv)		1	
5. (i)	× 4	1	
(ii)	*examples:* 1 ——————> 4 2 ——————> 8 3 ——————> 12	3	
6. (i)	output = input minus two	2	accept '2 less than the input'
(ii)	*examples:* 2 ——————> 0 3 ——————> 1 4 ——————> 2	3	

ALGEBRA C

Q.	Answer	Mark	Additional Guidance
(iii)	*example:* 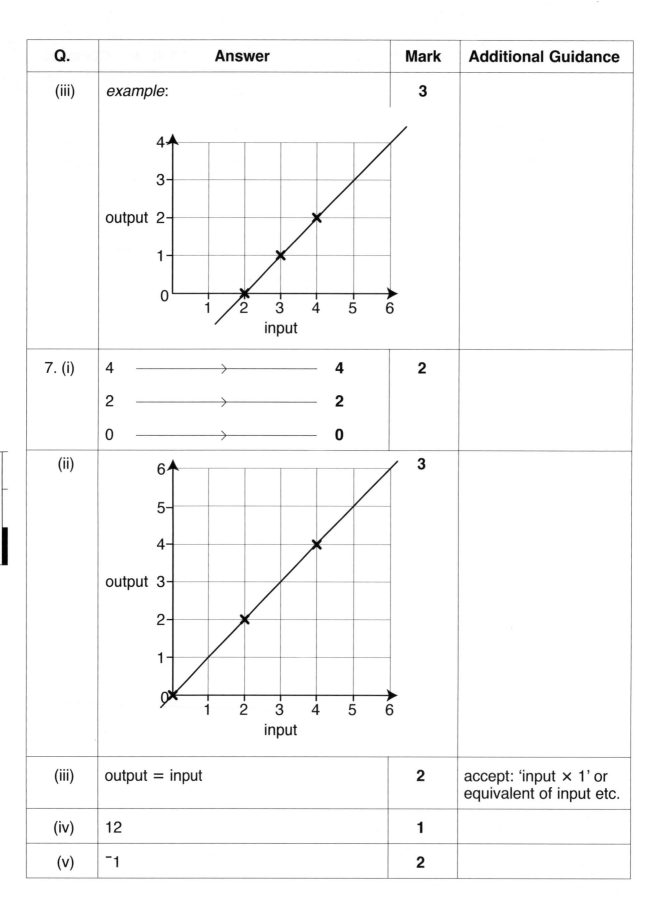	3	
7. (i)	4 ————→ **4** 2 ————→ **2** 0 ————→ **0**	2	
(ii)		3	
(iii)	output = input	2	accept: 'input × 1' or equivalent of input etc.
(iv)	12	1	
(v)	⁻1	2	

Q.	Answer	Mark	Additional Guidance
8. (i)	*examples:* 0 ———————→——————— 5 1 ———————→——————— 4 2 ———————→——————— 3	3	
(ii)	always five	2	
(iii)	output = **five** minus input	1	
9. (i)	3 ———————→——————— **7** **7** ———————→——————— 3 5 ———————→——————— **5**	3	
(ii)		3	

Q.	Answer	Mark	Additional Guidance
10. (i)	£10.50	**2**	
(ii)	6	**2**	
11. (i)(a)	20 pence	**1**	
(b)	200 pence	**1**	
(ii)	48 pence	**2**	
(iii)	24	**2**	
(iv)	*see opposite*	**4**	

ALGEBRA C

11.(iv)

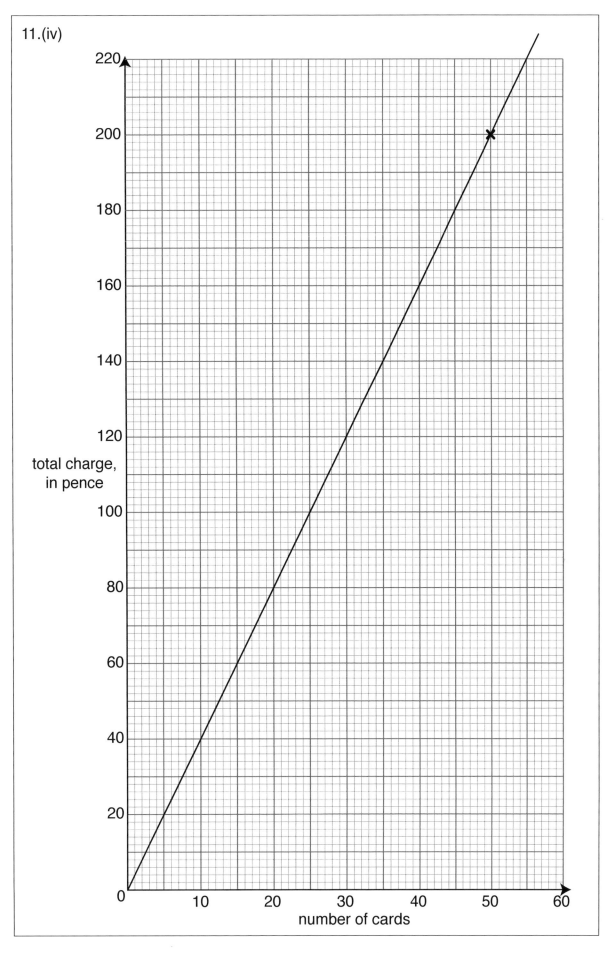

total charge, in pence

number of cards

ALGEBRA
C

Q.	Answer	Mark	Additional Guidance
12. (i)		3	

time taken, in hours	1	2	3	4	5	6	7	8
distance travelled, in miles	20	40	60	80	100	120	140	160

Q.	Answer	Mark	Additional Guidance
(ii)		4	

Q.	Answer	Mark	Additional Guidance
(iii)	150 miles	2	
13. (i)	34 francs	2	
(ii)	£6.40	2	
14. (i)	number of pesetas = **sixty times** number of dollars	2	
(ii)(a)	60	1	
(b)	300	1	

Q.	Answer	Mark	Additional Guidance
(iii)		3	

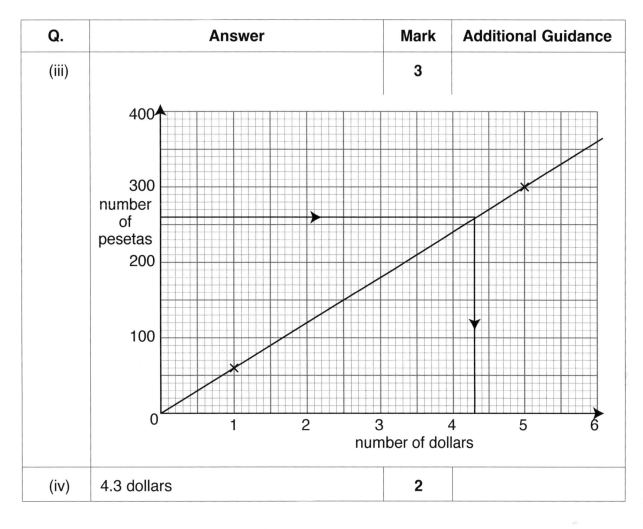

Q.	Answer	Mark	Additional Guidance
(iv)	4.3 dollars	2	

STRAND 5: SHAPE, SPACE AND MEASURES

A Measures

Q.	Answer	Mark	Additional Guidance
1.	D A C E B	**2**	
2.	E B A C F D	**3**	
3. (i)	70	**1**	
(ii)	60	**1**	
(iii)	1 cupful 7 large spoonfuls 1 small spoonful	**3**	
4. (i)	mm	**1**	
(ii)	km	**1**	
(iii)	m	**1**	
5. (i)	g	**1**	
(ii)	kg	**1**	
(iii)	tonne	**1**	
6. (i)	cm^2	**1**	
(ii)	ha	**1**	
(iii)	mm^2	**1**	
(iv)	m^2	**1**	

Q.	Answer	Mark	Additional Guidance
7. (i)	minutes	1	
(ii)	km	1	
(iii)	cm	1	
(iv)	m	1	
(v)	mm	1	
(vi)	g	1	
(vii)	g	1	
(viii)	mℓ	1	
8. (i)	cm	1	
(ii)	kg	1	
(iii)	km	1	
(iv)	ℓ	1	
(v)	mm	1	
(vi)	g	1	
9. (i)(a)	2 m	1	
(b)	120 g	1	
(c)	250 mℓ	1	
(ii)	*answers vary*	1	accept any reasonable estimate
10. (i)	100 cm^2	1	
(ii)	20 ℓ	1	
11. (i)	70 cm	1	
(ii)	1.25 litres	1	

SHAPE ETC A

Q.	Answer	Mark	Additional Guidance
12. (i)	0.6 litres	1	
(ii)	8 mm	1	
(iii)	3500 g	2	
(iv)	1.25 m	2	
13.	**1.02** m is the same as 102 cm or **1020** mm	2	
14. (i)	1.65 kg	4	
(ii)	1.485 kg	3	
15. (i)	Mary	2	
(ii)	5 g	2	
16. (i)	2.23 kg	2	
(ii)	2230 g	1	
17. (i)	Sarah's	1	
(ii)	David's and Mary's	2	
(iii)	160 cm	2	
18. (i)	approx 136 mm	1	
(ii)	approx 13.6 cm	1	
19.	23 cm	3	
20. (i)	2.25 m	1	
(ii)	9 m	2	
21. (i)	John's	1	
(ii)	72 mm	2	
22. (i)	153 cm	2	
(ii)	1.53 m	1	

Q.	Answer	Mark	Additional Guidance
23. (i)	1830 mm	1	
(ii)	1.83 m	1	
24. (i)	1.5 litres	1	
(ii)	1.005 litres	2	
(iii)	4.05 litres	2	
(iv)	0.95 litre	2	
25.	200 spoonfuls	2	
26.	125 mℓ	2	
27.	(ii) 0.3 litre and (iii) 300 mℓ	2	
28.	**C** 	2	
29. (i)	5000 mℓ	2	
(ii)	3	2	allow $2\frac{1}{2}$
30. (i)	109 mℓ	2	
(ii)	7 times	2	
(iii)(a)	1250 millilitres	2	
(b)	1.25 litres	1	

Q.	Answer	Mark	Additional Guidance
31. (i)	Angela **45** cm	1	
	George **49** cm	2	
	Henry **78** cm	2	
	Judy **46** cm	2	
(ii)	2.18 m	2	
(iii)	282 cm	2	
32.	120 g	2	
33.	3.86 kg	2	
34. (i)	68 cm	1	
(ii)	680 mm	1	
(iii)	0.68 m	1	
35. (i)	2736 g	2	
(ii)	3 kg	1	
36. (i)	600 g	2	
(ii)	450 g	2	
(iii)	150 g	2	
37.	2 kg 600 g	2	
38. (i)	100	1	
(ii)	7.25 g	2	
39.	approx 7.9 cm	2	
40. (i)	936 g	2	
(ii)	718 g	2	

SHAPE ETC A

Q.	Answer	Mark	Additional Guidance
41. (i)	50 mℓ	2	
(ii)	25 mℓ	2	
(iii)	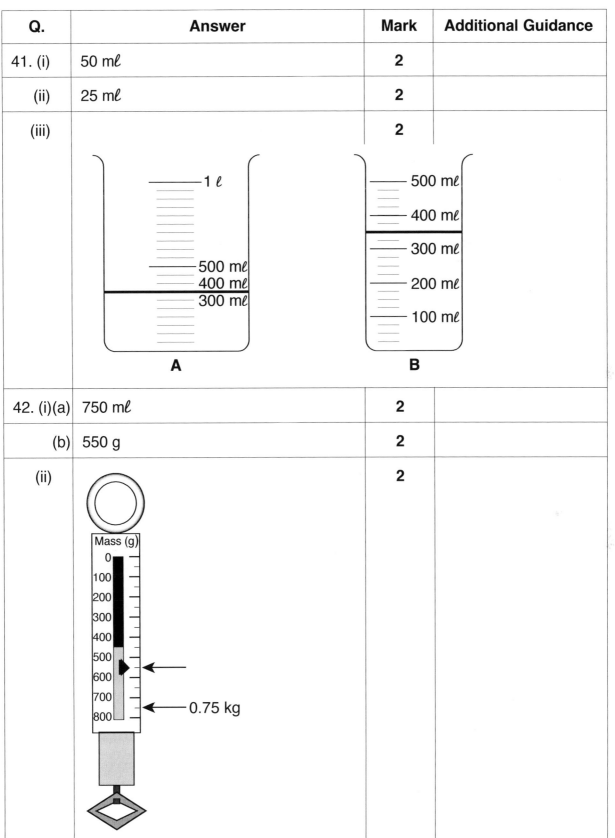	2	
42. (i)(a)	750 mℓ	2	
(b)	550 g	2	
(ii)		2	

SHAPE ETC

Q.	Answer	Mark	Additional Guidance
(iii)(a)	55 g	1	
(b)	1000 g	1	
43.	17.7 cm 18.1 cm 18.9 cm 19.5 cm	4	
44. (i)	each little division on scale **A** shows **10** grams	2	
	arrow **W** shows a mass of **30** grams	1	
	arrow **X** shows a mass of **180** grams	1	
(ii)	 scale **A**	2	
(iii)	each little division on scale **B** shows **25** grams	2	
	arrow **Y** shows a mass of **75** grams	1	
	arrow **Z** shows a mass of **150** grams	1	
(iv)	 scale **B**	2	
45. (i)	74	2	
(ii)	27	2	

Q.	Answer	Mark	Additional Guidance
46. (i)	32 kg	1	
(ii)	4 kg	2	
(iii)	3	2	
47. (i)	19 °C	1	
(ii)	15 °C	1	
(iii)	17 °C	2	
(iv)		2	
(v)	*see above*	2	
48.	11 degrees	2	
49.	‾2 °C	2	
50.	8 degrees	2	
51.	6 °C	2	
52. (i)	‾1 °C	1	
(ii)		2	either mercury shaded in or arrow etc.
53.	13 degrees	2	
54.	10 degrees	2	
55.	5 °C	1	
56. (i)	4 °C	1	

SHAPE ETC A

Q.	Answer	Mark	Additional Guidance
(ii)	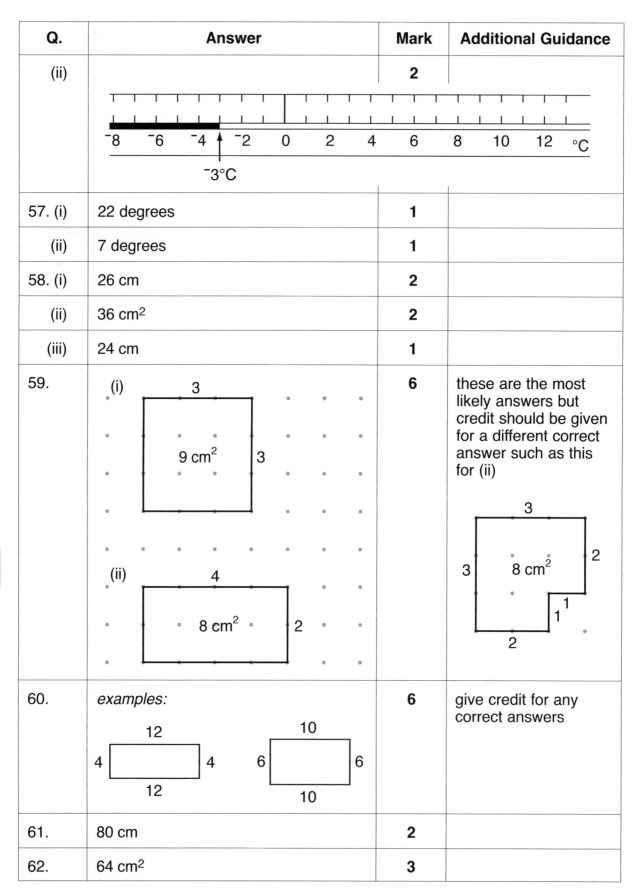	**2**	
57. (i)	22 degrees	**1**	
(ii)	7 degrees	**1**	
58. (i)	26 cm	**2**	
(ii)	36 cm²	**2**	
(iii)	24 cm	**1**	
59.		**6**	these are the most likely answers but credit should be given for a different correct answer such as this for (ii)
60.	*examples:*	**6**	give credit for any correct answers
61.	80 cm	**2**	
62.	64 cm²	**3**	

Q.	Answer	Mark	Additional Guidance
63.	72 m	2	
64. (i)	tennis **264** m^2 netball **450** m^2 volleyball **162** m^2	6	
(ii)	13 m	2	
65. (i)	30 m	2	
(ii)	36 m^2	2	
(iii)	6 m	2	
66.	125 m	4	
67. (i)(a)	24 m	2	
(b)	22 m^2	3	
(ii)	36 cm	3	
(iii)	9 cm	3	
68. (i)	480 cm^2	2	
(ii)	240 cm^2	2	
(iii)	notebook area is half of the textbook area	2	
69. (i)	1000 cm^2	2	
(ii)	150 cm	2	
(iii)	1.5 m	1	
(iv)	£3.45	3	
70. (i)	20 m	1	
(ii)	$AB =$ **8** cm $BC =$ **5** cm	2	

Q.	Answer	Mark	Additional Guidance
(iii)	$AB =$ **160** m $BC =$ **100** m	2	
(iv)	16 000 m²	2	
71.	22.5 cm²	3	
72. (i)	1200 mm	3	
(ii)	3.3 m	4	
73. (i)	24 cm	2	
(ii)	24 cm²	2	
74. (i)	46 m²	3	
(ii)	£486	2	
(iii)	30 m	3	
75.	**A** = 12 cubes	1	
	B = 12 cubes	2	
76.	70	2	
77. (i)	48 cm³	3	
(ii)	4 cuboids	2	
(iii)	*example:*	3	
78.	420 cubes	4	

Q.	Answer	Mark	Additional Guidance
79. (i)	4	2	
(ii)	16	2	
80. (i)	216 cm^3	2	
(ii)	1 × 2 × 4 2 × 2 × 2	4	
81. (i)	**D A C B**	3	
(ii)	76	2	
82. (i)	8:25 am	2	
(ii)	08:25	1	
(iii)	20 minutes	2	
83.	16:10	2	
84.	19:29	1	
85. (i)	50 minutes	1	
(ii)	180 minutes	1	
(iii)	$\frac{5}{18}$	1	
86.	33 minutes	2	
87.	25 minutes	2	
88.	32 minutes	2	
89.	2 minutes	2	

SHAPE ETC A

Q.	Answer				Mark	Additional Guidance
90. (i)			starts	ends	5	
		assembly	**08:55**	09:15		
		lesson 1	09:15	09:50		
		lesson 2	09:50	**10:25**		
		break	**10:25**	**10:45**		
		lesson 3	**10:45**	**11:20**		
		lesson 4	**11:20**	**11:55**		
(ii)	70 minutes				2	
(iii)	35 minutes				1	
91. (i)	09:00 to 09:15 Assembly				6	
	09:15 to 09:50 Maths					
	09:50 to **10:25** Maths					
	10:25 to **10:40** Break					
	10:40 to **11:15** English					
	11:15 to **11:50** English					
	11:50 to **12:25** History					
	12:25 to 13:35 Lunch break					
(ii)	15:20				3	
92. (i)	40 minutes				2	
(ii)	08:50				1	
(iii)	08:10				1	

SHAPE ETC A

Q.	Answer	Mark	Additional Guidance
(iv)	17:25	2	
93. (i)	Channel B	1	
(ii)	55 minutes	2	
(iii)	35 minutes	2	
(iv)	20 minutes	3	
94.	1 hour 37 minutes	2	
95.	1 hour 15 minutes	2	
96. (i)	08:18	3	
(ii)	7 hours 35 minutes	2	
(iii)	18:47	3	
97. (i)	Mary	1	
(ii)	10.8 seconds	2	
98. (i)	8 km	2	
(ii)	16 km	1	
99.	100 seconds	4	
100.(i)	1 hour 15 minutes	2	
(ii)	19:05	2	
101.	Susan walking Jenny flying John cycling Ian motoring	4	
102.(i)	John	1	
(ii)	17 months	2	
103.	22 days	2	
104.	*answers vary*	2	

Q.	Answer	Mark	Additional Guidance
105.	2 November	2	
106.	AD 9	2	
107.(i)	goes to bed 9:00 pm gets up 8:25 am	1 1	
(ii)	goes to bed 21:00 gets up 08:25	1 1	
(iii)	11 hours 25 minutes	2	
(iv)	12 hours 35 minutes	2	
108.(i)	10:20	2	
(ii)	18:15	2	
109.	52 hours 45 minutes	3	
110.(i)	15 cm	1	
(ii)	puppies do not sit still! puppies can stretch!	2	allow any suitable answer
(iii)		2	line should not really be straight
(iv)	there are intermediate values between those recorded; growth is not in steady increases	2	or any suitable answer

Q.	Answer	Mark	Additional Guidance
111. (i)	the little lines at the ends have width all measurements are approximate and depend upon limitations of the equipment and the human eye	2	
(ii)(a)	approx 7.8 cm	1	it should be accepted that all measurements of living things are difficult to take and can only be approximate
(b)	approx 6.5 cm	1	
112. (i)		2	
(ii)	meniscus on water surface difficulty of pouring a little water at a time water wets the sides of the jars it is almost impossible to pour all the water from jar **A** etc.	2	answers vary
113. (i)	360 grams	1	
(ii)	it would be difficult to measure **exactly** 140 grams of plasticine	2	

SHAPE ETC

B Shape

Q.	Answer	Mark	Additional Guidance
1. (i)	P S S P S P S P	4	
(ii)	**A** regular octagon **C** cone **E** sphere **G** triangular prism	4	accept octagon
2.	square pyramid	2	
3. (i)	kite cube cylinder	3	
(ii)	*examples:* 	2	any suitable triangle
4.	5 sides	1	
5.	square rectangle rhombus parallelogram kite trapezium	2	any two
6.	4 sides	1	

Q.	Answer	Mark	Additional Guidance
7.	<table><tr><td>number of sides</td><td>name of polygon</td></tr><tr><td>3</td><td>triangle</td></tr><tr><td>4</td><td>**quadrilateral**</td></tr><tr><td>5</td><td>**pentagon**</td></tr><tr><td>6</td><td>**hexagon**</td></tr><tr><td>7</td><td>**heptagon**</td></tr><tr><td>8</td><td>**octagon**</td></tr></table>	5	
8. (i)	both quadrilaterals (4 sides)	2	
(ii)	both have 2 lines of symmetry and rotational symmetry of order 2	2	
9.	cylinder	2	
10. (i)	equilateral	1	
(ii)		3	
11.	rhombus	2	
12. (i)	circle, because it does not have straight edges	2	
(ii)	trapezium, because it is a plane shape and the others are solid shapes	2	

Q.	Answer	Mark	Additional Guidance
13. (i)	**A** hexagon **C** square **F** rhombus **H** parallelogram	4	
(ii)	right-angled isosceles triangle	2	
(iii)	shape A and shape **D** are congruent	1	
(iv)	shape **E** and shape **H** are congruent	2	or **B** and **G**
14. (i)	**A** rhombus **B** kite		
(ii)	A B	2	
(iii)	**A** order 2 **B** order 1 (no rotational symmetry)	2	
15. (i)	isosceles triangle	2	
(ii)	rhombus	2	
16. (i)	**A** kite	1	
	B parallelogram	1	
	C hexagon	1	
(ii)(a)	**A** and **C**	1	

Q.	Answer	Mark	Additional Guidance
(b)		**2**	
(iii)	**B** and **C** (both order 2)	**2**	
17. (i)	regular pentagon	**1**	
(ii)		**2**	
(iii)	this shape has rotational symmetry about its centre point of order **5**	**2**	
18. (i)	rectangle rhombus	**2**	
(ii)		**2**	

Q.	Answer	Mark	Additional Guidance
19. (i)	**A** pentagon	1	
	B hexagon	1	
(ii)	isosceles	1	
(iii)	 **shape B** **shape C** **shape D**	3	
20. (i)	parallelogram	1	
(ii)(a)	*see below*	1	
(b)		1	
21. (i)	rhombus kite	2	
(ii)		2	

Q.	Answer	Mark	Additional Guidance
22.		2	
23. (i)	**A B C E**	3	
(ii)	**C**	1	
24. (i)		2	
(ii)(a)		3	
(b)	once	1	
25. (i)		5	

Q.	Answer	Mark	Additional Guidance
(ii)	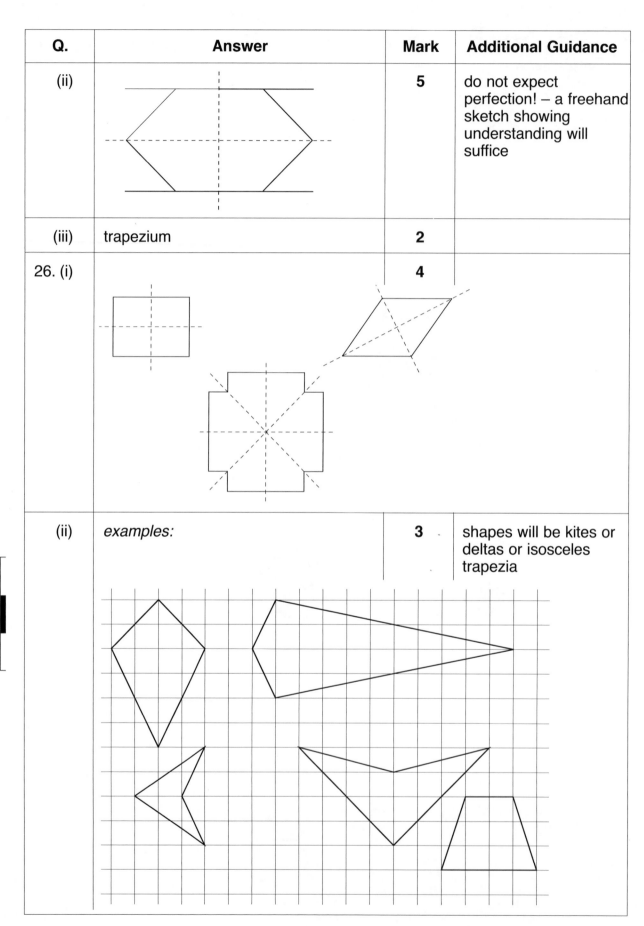	**5**	do not expect perfection! – a freehand sketch showing understanding will suffice
(iii)	trapezium	**2**	
26. (i)		**4**	
(ii)	*examples:*	**3**	shapes will be kites or deltas or isosceles trapezia

Q.	Answer	Mark	Additional Guidance
27. (i)(a)	quadrilaterals	1	
(b)	shape **B** is a **rhombus**	6	
	shape **C** is a **parallelogram**		
	shape **A** has **4** lines of symmetry		
	shape **C** has **no** lines of symmetry		
	shape **D** has rotational symmetry of order **2**		
	the diagonals of shape **B are at right angles (or perpendicular)** to one another		
(ii)		3	
28.		4	

Q.	Answer	Mark	Additional Guidance
29.		6	
30. (i)	**C** **F** **H** **I**	2	
(ii)	**A** **C** **D** **G** **H** **J**	2	
(iii)	**A** **B** **F**	2	
31. (i)	**D**	2	
(ii)	*example:*	2	

Q.	Answer	Mark	Additional Guidance
32. (i)(a)	shape **D** is a square	**1**	
(b)	shape **C** is a parallelogram	**1**	
(ii)(a)	**B** and **E**	**2**	
(b)	*examples:* **A** and **B**, **B** and **D**, **C** and **E** etc.	**2**	if **C** is turned upside down, it makes an isosceles trapezium with **A**
(c)	**B** and **E**	**2**	
(d)	*examples:* **B**, **D** and **E**, **B**, **C** and **E**, **A**, **B** and **E** etc.	**2**	
33. (i)	*example:* 	**3**	
(ii)	*example:* 	**3**	

SHAPE ETC
B

Q.	Answer	Mark	Additional Guidance
(iii)	*example:*	3	
(iv)	*answers vary*	5	
34. (i)	**A** **D** **G**	2	
(ii)	**H** **J** **L**	2	
(iii)	**D** **E** *or* **D** **I**	2	
(iv)	**A** **B** **F**	2	
35. (i)	6	1	
(ii)(a)	5	1	
(b)	4	1	
(iii)	2 3 4 5	2	
36. (i)	64	2	
(ii)	32 cm^3	1	
(iii)	3 cm	2	

Q.	Answer	Mark	Additional Guidance
(iv)		3	or suitable alternative
(v)	52 cm²	3	
37. (i)	**A**	3	
(ii)	*example:* 	3	answers vary a freehand sketch is expected

SHAPE ETC B

Q.	Answer	Mark	Additional Guidance
38.	*example:*	4	or suitable alternative

Q.	Answer	Mark	Additional Guidance
39. (i)	*example:*	5	answers vary
(ii)	30	2	
(iii)	*examples:* 10 cm by 1 cm by 3 cm 5 cm by 1 cm by 6 cm 15 cm by 1 cm by 2 cm	3	

SHAPE ETC
B

Q.	Answer	Mark	Additional Guidance
40. (i)	tetrahedron	**2**	
(ii)		**3**	

| 41. | | **3** | |

SHAPE ETC
B

Q.	Answer	Mark	Additional Guidance
42. (i)		3	
(ii)	pentagonal prism	2	

SHAPE ETC
B

C Space

Q.	Answer	Mark	Additional Guidance
1.	*A* (3, 1) *B* (4, 5) *C* (1, 7) *D* (7, 3) *E* (2, 5) *F* (0, 4) *G* (6, 0) *H* (7, 6)	8	
2. (i)		3	
(ii)	*see above*	2	
(iii)	(2, 0)	2	

Q.	Answer	Mark	Additional Guidance
3. (i)		2	
(ii)	*see above*	2	
(iii)	(5, 4)	1	
4. (i)	*A* (1, 4) *B* (5, 7) *C* (9, 4) *D* (5, 1)	4	
(ii)	(5, 4)	1	

Q.	Answer	Mark	Additional Guidance
5. (i)		2	

(ii)	*see above*	2	
(iii)	*see above*	2	
(iv)	yes, order 2	1	
(v)	12 cm^2	2	

Q.	Answer	Mark	Additional Guidance
6. (i)	*see below* (shape **B**)	2	

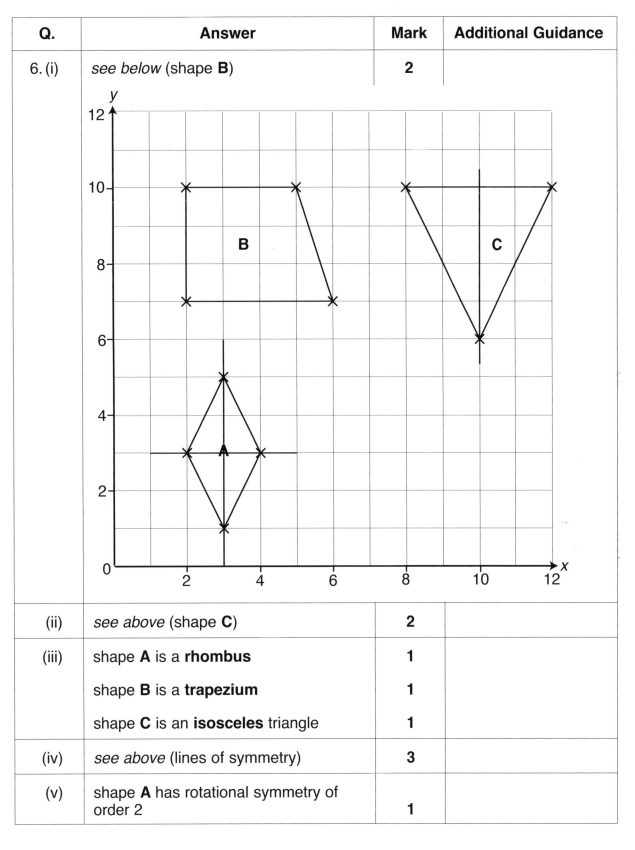

(ii)	*see above* (shape **C**)	2	
(iii)	shape **A** is a **rhombus**	1	
	shape **B** is a **trapezium**	1	
	shape **C** is an **isosceles** triangle	1	
(iv)	*see above* (lines of symmetry)	3	
(v)	shape **A** has rotational symmetry of order 2	1	

Q.	Answer	Mark	Additional Guidance
7. (i)	A (4, 2) B (0, 4)	2	
(ii)	4	1	
(iii)	4	2	
(iv)	(2, 3)	2	
(v)	12 cm²	1	
(vi)	16 cm	2	
8. (i)		4	
(ii)	pentagon	1	
(iii)	AE and AB AB and BC	1	
(iv)	AE and BC	1	
(v)	see above (line of symmetry)	2	
(vi)	16 cm²	3	

Q.	Answer	Mark	Additional Guidance
9. (i)		2	

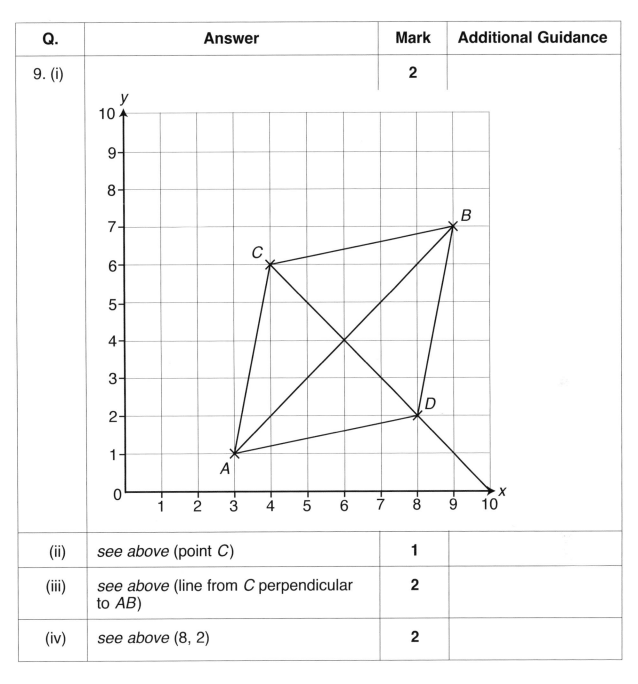

(ii)	*see above* (point *C*)	1	
(iii)	*see above* (line from *C* perpendicular to *AB*)	2	
(iv)	*see above* (8, 2)	2	

SHAPE ETC
C

Q.	Answer	Mark	Additional Guidance
10.	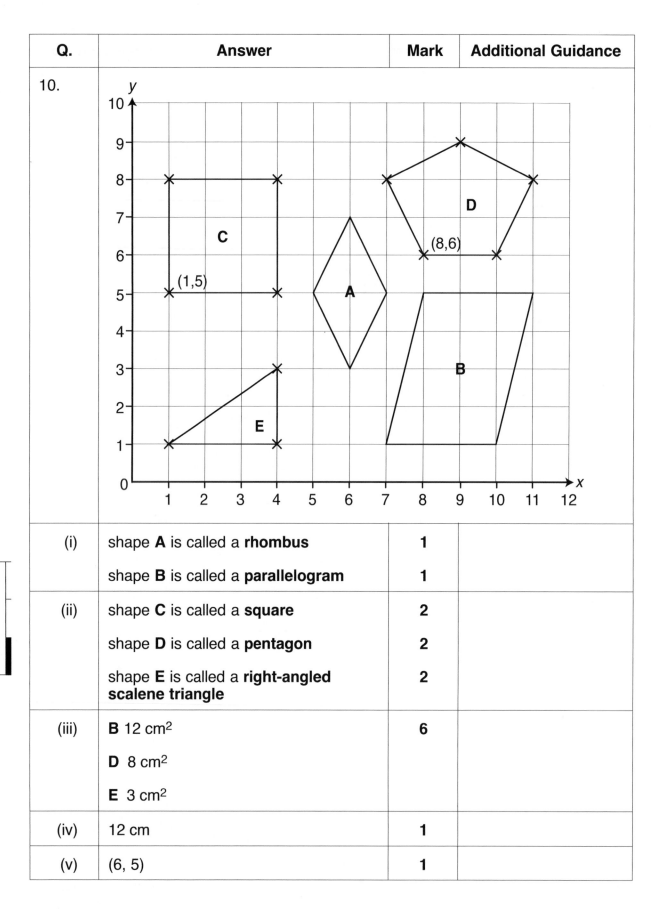		
(i)	shape **A** is called a **rhombus**	1	
	shape **B** is called a **parallelogram**	1	
(ii)	shape **C** is called a **square**	2	
	shape **D** is called a **pentagon**	2	
	shape **E** is called a **right-angled scalene triangle**	2	
(iii)	**B** 12 cm²	6	
	D 8 cm²		
	E 3 cm²		
(iv)	12 cm	1	
(v)	(6, 5)	1	

Q.	Answer	Mark	Additional Guidance
11. (i)	B (4, ⁻1)	1	
	C (⁻5, 1)	1	
	D (⁻2, ⁻3)	1	
(ii)		4	

Q.	Answer	Mark	Additional Guidance
12.(i)(a)	A (⁻2, 4)	1	
	B (4, 1)	1	
	C (⁻2, ⁻2)	1	
	D (⁻3, 1)	1	

Q.	Answer	Mark	Additional Guidance
(b)	kite	1	
(ii)(a)		2	
(b)	rhombus	1	
13. (i)		2	
(ii)	SE	1	
(iii)	E	3	

Q.	Answer	Mark	Additional Guidance
14. (i)	180°	**1**	
(ii)	**C**	**2**	
15.		**4**	
16. (i)	200 m	**1**	
(ii)	SW	**1**	
(iii)	*see below* (position of *C*)	**2**	
(iv)	*see above* (position of *D*)	**1**	
(v)	approx 460 m	**2**	

Q.	Answer	Mark	Additional Guidance
17. (i)	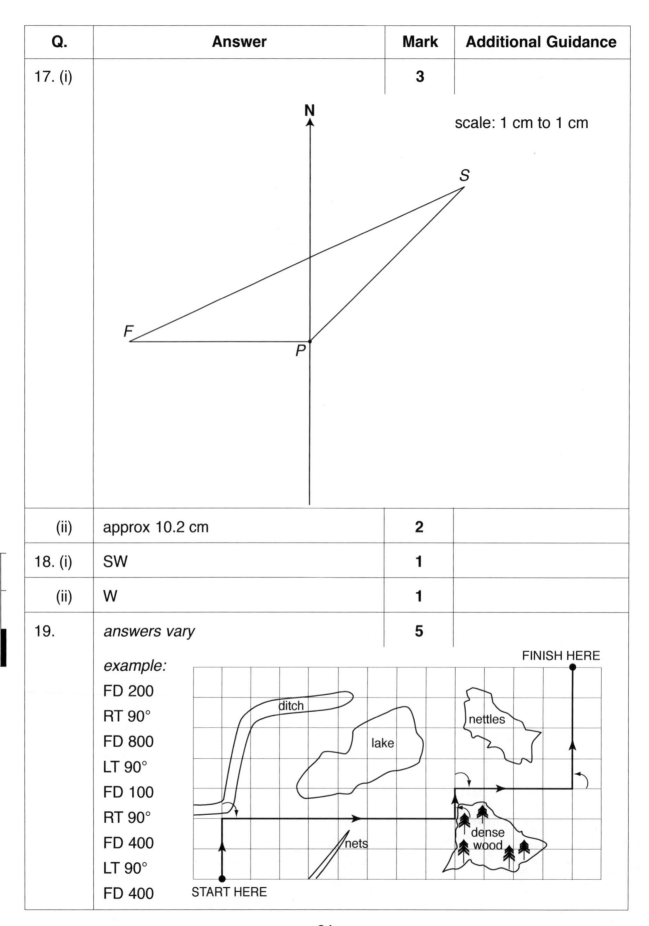	3	
(ii)	approx 10.2 cm	2	
18. (i)	SW	1	
(ii)	W	1	
19.	*answers vary* *example:* FD 200 RT 90° FD 800 LT 90° FD 100 RT 90° FD 400 LT 90° FD 400	5	

Q.	Answer	Mark	Additional Guidance
20. (i)	(parallel line)	1	

(ii)	*see above* (perpendicular through Z)	1	
21. (i)		1	

(ii)	less	1	
22. (i)	right	1	
(ii)	obtuse	1	
(iii)	reflex	1	
23. (i)	60°	1	in all angle measurements allow ±1°
(ii)	112°	1	
24. (i)	horizontal	1	
(ii)	acute	1	
(iii)	vertical	1	
(iv)	perpendicular	1	
(v)	parallel	1	

Q.	Answer	Mark	Additional Guidance
25.	*example:* 	2	
26. (i)(a)	C	1	
(b)	B	1	
(c)	A or D	1	
(d)	E	1	
(ii)	pentagon	1	
27.	acute	2	
28. (i)	143 degrees	1	
(ii)	obtuse	1	
29.	$p = 50°$ $q = 85°$	2 2	pupils will probably extend the sides of the triangle to make the measurements easier
30.	angle *L* is **an obtuse** angle of about **120°** angle *M* is **a reflex** angle of about **280°** angle *N* is **a right** angle of **90°** angle *O* is **an acute** angle of about **40°**	6	
31. (i)	90 degrees	2	
(ii)	A	1	*B* has longer arms
32. (i)	reflex	1	
(ii)	300°	2	
33.	the angles of a triangle add up to 180° (a half turn)	2	

Q.	Answer	Mark	Additional Guidance
34. (i)	60°	1	
(ii)	140°	2	
(iii)	70°	2	
(iv)	100°	2	
35. (i)	(circle, centre *C*, radius 2.8 cm)	1	

(ii)	*see above* (arc, centre *C*, radius 10 cm)	1	
36. (i)		4	

(ii)	32 degrees	2	

Q.	Answer	Mark	Additional Guidance
37. (i)	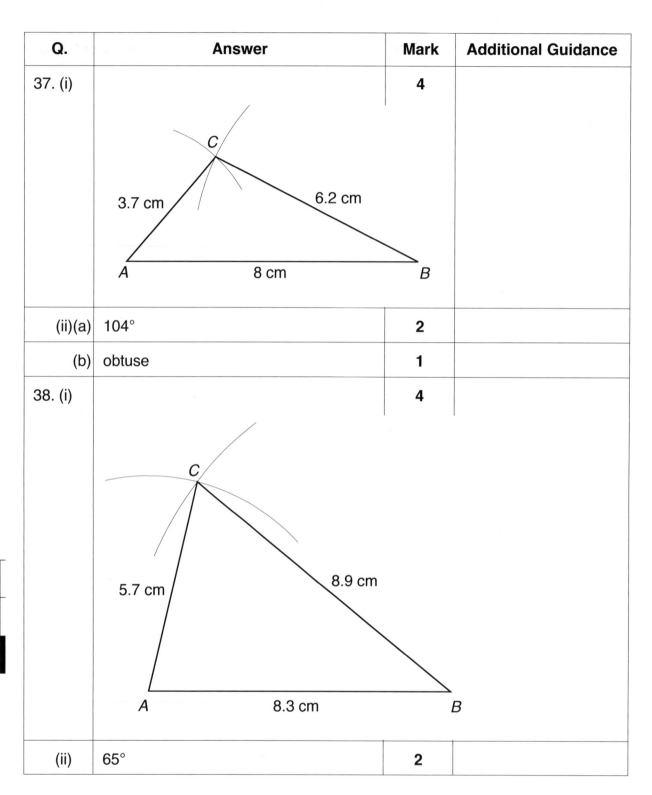	4	
(ii)(a)	104°	2	
(b)	obtuse	1	
38. (i)		4	
(ii)	65°	2	

Q.	Answer	Mark	Additional Guidance
39. (i)		**5**	
(ii)	*see above* (angles marked A or O)	**3**	
40. (i)		**4**	
(ii)	9.1 cm	**2**	

Q.	Answer	Mark	Additional Guidance
41. (i)		**4**	

(ii)	acute (47°)	**1**	
(iii)	approx 9.5 cm	**1**	
(iv)	approx 26 cm	**2**	

Q.	Answer	Mark	Additional Guidance
42. (i)		3	
(ii)	$BAC = 43°$	1	
	$ACB = 62°$	1	
(iii)	approx 9.3 cm	1	
(iv)	approx 24.4 cm	2	

SHAPE ETC

Q.	Answer	Mark	Additional Guidance
43. (i)	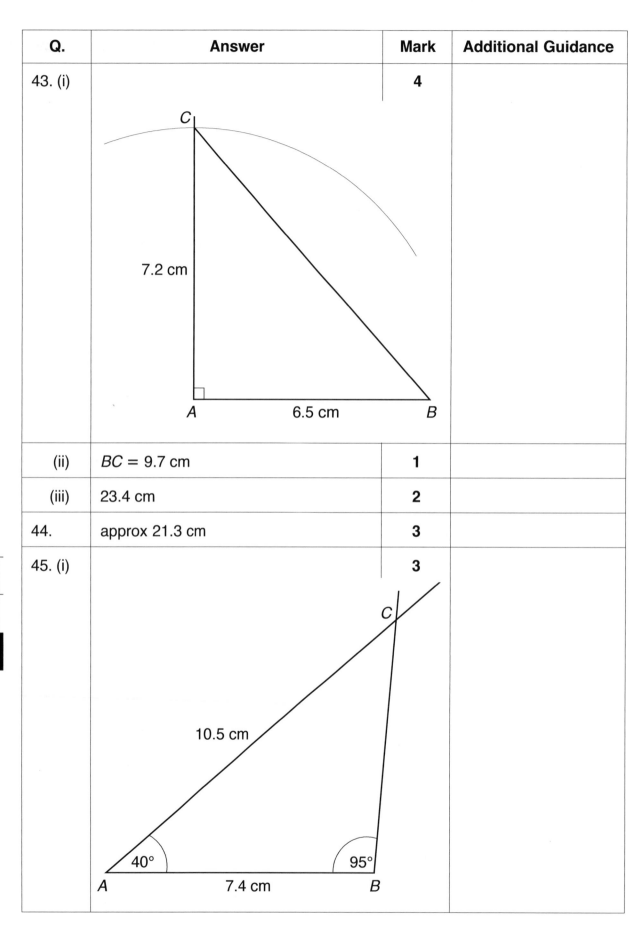	4	
(ii)	BC = 9.7 cm	1	
(iii)	23.4 cm	2	
44.	approx 21.3 cm	3	
45. (i)		3	

Q.	Answer	Mark	Additional Guidance
(ii)	AC = 10.5 cm	**1**	
46. (i)(a)	PR 10 cm	**1**	
	QR 5 cm	**1**	
(b)	isosceles (2 sides of 10 cm)	**1**	
(ii)(a)		**1**	
(b)	isosceles trapezium	**2**	
47. (i)		**4**	
(ii)	ACB = 70°	**1**	
	BC = 7.7 cm	**1**	

Q.	Answer	Mark	Additional Guidance
48. (i)	*examples:*	4	
(ii)	*examples:*	4	

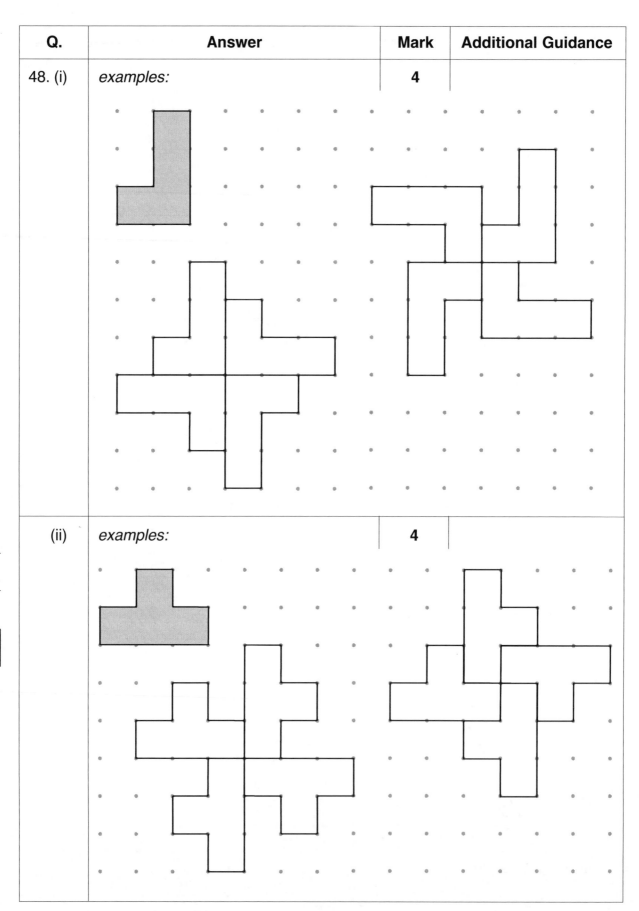

Q.	Answer	Mark	Additional Guidance
(iii)	*examples:*	4	
49. (i)	translation	1	
(ii)	reflection	1	
(iii)	rotation	1	
50. (i)		2	
(ii)		2	

C

Q.	Answer	Mark	Additional Guidance
(iii)	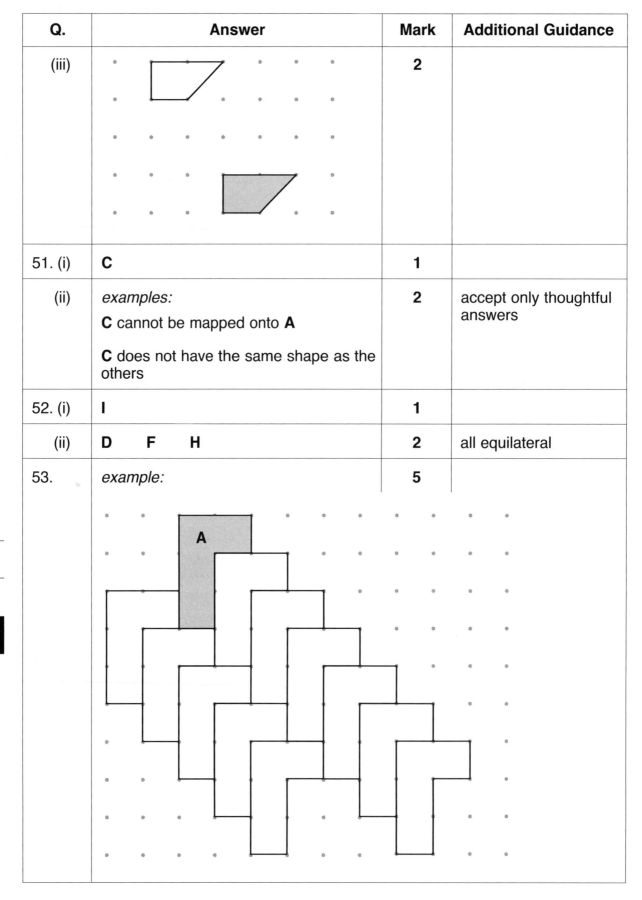	2	
51. (i)	**C**	1	
(ii)	*examples:* **C** cannot be mapped onto **A** **C** does not have the same shape as the others	2	accept only thoughtful answers
52. (i)	**I**	1	
(ii)	**D** **F** **H**	2	all equilateral
53.	*example:*	5	

Q.	Answer	Mark	Additional Guidance
54. (i)(a)	reflection	1	
(b)	rotation	1	
(c)	translation	1	
(ii)	congruent	2	

SHAPE ETC
C

STRAND 6: HANDLING DATA

A Data handling

Q.	Answer	Mark	Additional Guidance
1.		4	black heads spots
2.	**A**	2	
3.	C B F A E D	4	
4.	A C E B D F	4	
5.	15 6 9 13 17 8 10 25	4	

DATA A

78

Q.	Answer	Mark	Additional Guidance
6.	*example:*	**6**	

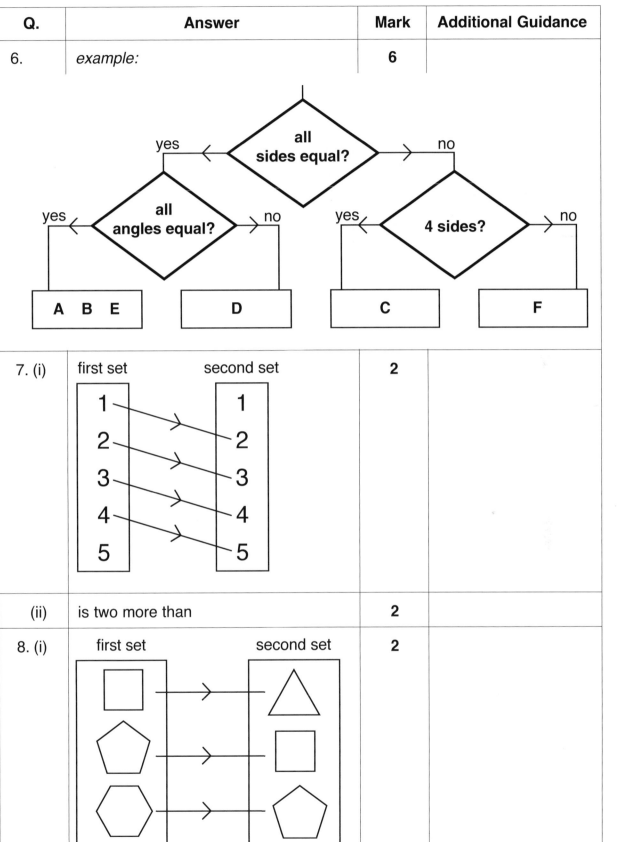

Q.	Answer	Mark	Additional Guidance
7. (i)	first set second set	**2**	
(ii)	is two more than	**2**	
8. (i)	first set second set	**2**	

79

Q.	Answer	Mark	Additional Guidance
8.(ii)	first set second set	2	
(iii)	first set second set	2	
9. (i)	Colin	1	
(ii)	Anna	1	
(iii)	Anna	1	
(iv)	3	1	
(v)	**NAME:** *David* **AGE:** *9* **SEX** (M/F): *m* **MASS** (kg): *37* **HEIGHT** (cm): *140* **WAIST** (cm): *59*	2	

DATA A

Q.	Answer	Mark	Additional Guidance
(vi)	NAME: *Ben* AGE: *10* SEX (M/F): *M* MASS (kg): *34* HEIGHT (cm): *142* WAIST (cm): *62*	2	
(vii)	NAME: *Gina* AGE: *9* SEX (M/F): *F* MASS (kg): *31* HEIGHT (cm): *143* WAIST (cm): *69*	2	
10. (i)	Jane	1	
(ii)	Tom	2	
11. (i)	Janet, Polly	2	
(ii)	50%	3	
(iii)	Phil	2	
(iv)	10	2	
(v)	14 cm	2	
(vi)	Bob	2	
12. (i)		4	

	Monday	Tuesday	Wednesday	Thursday	Friday
adults	2147	3026	1721	**1223**	5000
children	3927	5121	3000	2446	**15 000**

Q.	Answer	Mark	Additional Guidance
(ii)	29 494	4	
(iii)	6000	2	

DATA A

Q.	Answer	Mark	Additional Guidance
13. (i)		3	

	long legs	not long legs
not black	B	C
black	D	A

| (ii) | | 4 | |

black   long legs

A (D) B

C

| (iii) | | 3 | |

beetle	black	long legs
A	✓	✗
B	✗	✔
C	✗	✗
D	✔	✔

| 14. (i) | | 4 | |

	prime	not prime
not even	3 5 7	1 9
even	2	4 6 8

| (ii) | | 4 | |

prime   even

3 5 7 (2) 4 6 8

1 9

DATA A

Q.	Answer	Mark	Additional Guidance
15.	11	**2**	9 + 2
16. (i)	4 girls	**2**	
(ii)	18 girls	**3**	
17. (i)	(Venn diagram: N and U overlapping circles, 7 in N only, 3 in intersection, 5 in U only)	**5**	
(ii)	3	**1**	
18. (i)	(Venn diagram: letters in the word **triangle** — t i n g l; intersection — a e r; letters in the word **square** — s q u)	**4**	
(ii)	a e r	**2**	
(iii)	q s u	**2**	

DATA A

Q.	Answer	Mark	Additional Guidance
19.		3	

no line symmetry	P	(triangle)
line symmetry	(square) R	E
	4 sides	not 4 sides

	20. (i)		4	

name	tally	total
Tina	⊥⊥⊥⊥ ⊥⊥⊥⊥ ⊥⊥⊥⊥ ||||	19
Sam	⊥⊥⊥⊥ ⊥⊥⊥⊥ ||	**12**
Kerry	⊥⊥⊥⊥ ⊥⊥⊥⊥ ⊥⊥⊥⊥ ⊥⊥⊥⊥ |||	**23**
Will	⊥⊥⊥⊥ |||	**8**
Jane	⊥⊥⊥⊥ ⊥⊥⊥⊥ ⊥⊥⊥⊥ ⊥⊥⊥⊥ ⊥⊥⊥⊥ ||	**27**

	(ii)	89	2	
	21. (i)		3	

	tally	total
Alan	⊥⊥⊥⊥ ||	7
Bertie	⊥⊥⊥⊥ ||||	9
Corrie	⊥⊥⊥⊥ |	6
Debbie	⊥⊥⊥⊥	5

84

Q.	Answer	Mark	Additional Guidance
(ii)	*see opposite* (total column)	2	
22. (i)	2	1	
(ii)	3	1	
(iii)	25	2	
(iv)	Colin and Ekwi *or* David and Fiona	2	
23. (i)	10	1	
(ii)	9	1	
(iii)	48	2	
(iv)	Alice and Eleanor	2	
24. (i)	260	2	
(ii)		2	

Key: ☐ represents 20 cassettes

pop	☐☐ ☐☐ ☐☐ ☐☐ ☐☐ ☐☐ ☐☐ ☐
classical	☐☐ ☐☐ ☐☐ ☐☐
spoken	☐☐ ◹
country and western	▨▨ ▨▨
other	☐

Q.	Answer	Mark	Additional Guidance
(iii)	spoken	2	
(iv)	570	3	
(v)(a)	330	2	
(b)	bought as Christmas presents	2	

DATA

Q.	Answer	Mark	Additional Guidance
25. (i)	16	2	
(ii)	Key: ● represents 4 cartons 	Monday	● ● ● ●
Tuesday	● ● ● ● ◖
Wednesday	● ● ●
Thursday	● ● ● ● ● ●
Friday	● ● ● ● ●		2	
(iii)	90	3	$22\frac{1}{2}$ × 4
(iv)	900	2	
26. (i)	£15	2	60 ÷ 4
(ii)	stage lighting and camera	5	20 symbols
(iii)	£240	3	16 × 15
(iv)	*answers vary*	1 3	for number of items for itemising the items
27. (i)	5	1	
(ii)	23	1	
(iii)	2	1	
(iv)	**B**	1	

DATA A

86

Q.	Answer	Mark	Additional Guidance
28. (i)	black white grey cube colour	3	
(ii)	*e.g.* one block to represent 3000 supporters	2	
29. (i)	*e.g.* because all the mice are 'all black' or 'all white' or 'black and white'	2	
(ii)	*e.g.* they both have four regions	2	
(iii)	*e.g.* they use symbols to represent the mice (the block and mouse symbol are equivalent)	2	
(iv)	$\frac{5}{11}$	1	
(v)	30%	2	$\frac{3}{10}$
30. (i)(a)	$\frac{1}{8}$	1	
(b)	$\frac{3}{8}$	1	
(c)	$\frac{1}{2}$	1	

Q.	Answer	Mark	Additional Guidance
(ii)(a)	50%	1	
(b)	12.5%	2	
(iii)		2	
(iv)	*example:* one block represents one slice Sarah John Tubby	4	
(v)	*answers vary*	4	accept any answer which is supported by a reasoned explanation
31. (i)(a)	**D**	1	
(b)	none	1	
(c)	20	2	
(d)	4	1	
(ii)	*examples:* numbers and label on the vertical axis bars are not split into blocks	1 1	
(iii)(a)	*example:* a pictogram would be more difficult to draw and take longer	2	

Q.		Answer	Mark	Additional Guidance
(b)		*example:* *the fraction 'bar' would be long and it would be difficult to see the result for group **E***	2	
(c)		*answers vary*	2	give credit for any thoughtful answer (see (ii))
32. (i)		200	3	68, 46, 34, 52
(ii)		16	2	
(iii)		$\frac{23}{100}$	2	
(iv)		34%	2	$\frac{68}{200} \times 100$
(v)		twice as many children **walk** to school as **cycle** to school	2	
33. (i)			4	

class	Mon.	Tue.	Wed.	Thu.	Fri.	total
1	2	1	0	1	0	4
2	3	2	1	2	1	9
3	0	2	3	2	4	**11**
4	2	3	3	1	1	10
5	1	**3**	0	2	20	**26**
total	8	11	7	**8**	26	**60**

Q.		Answer	Mark	Additional Guidance
(ii)		60	1	
(iii)		class 1	1	
(iv)		class 5	1	
(v)		Friday	1	
(vi)		class 1	1	

DATA A

Q.	Answer	Mark	Additional Guidance
(vii)		4	

number of absences

days of the week

34. (i)	February	1	
(ii)	October and November	2	
(iii)	10	2	
(iv)	*examples:* better weather, summer holidays etc.	2	
(v)(a)	December	1	
(b)	bought as Christmas presents	1	

Q.	Answer	Mark	Additional Guidance
35. (i)	320 g	**2**	
(ii)(a)	250 g	**1**	
(b)	0.25 kg	**2**	
(iii)	370 g	**3**	
(iv)		**2**	

mass (g) — puppy A, B, C, D, E, F

36. (i)	3 3 4 6 9	**2**	
(ii)(a)	6	**1**	
(b)	R**ANGE**	**1**	
(iii)(a)	4	**1**	
(b)	M**EDIAN**	**1**	
(iv)(a)	3	**1**	
(b)	**MO**DE	**1**	
(v)(a)	25	**2**	
(b)	5	**1**	
(c)	**MEA**N	**1**	

DATA A

Q.	Answer	Mark	Additional Guidance
37. (i)	7	1	
(ii)	5	2	
(iii)	6	1	
(iv)	5	3	$30 \div 6$
38. (i)	9 13 18 21 25 26 34	2	
(ii)	25	1	
(iii)	21	2	
39. (i)	3 hours	1	
(ii)	$2\frac{1}{2}$ hours	2	
(iii)	35 hours	3	
(iv)	5 hours	2	
40.	162 cm	4	total 810 mean 162
41.	54	2	total 108 mean 54

42. (i) **2**

score	0	1	2	3	4	5	6	7	8	9	10
tally			/	//	//	//	//	////	///	//	//

(ii) **2**

score	0	1	2	3	4	5	6	7	8	9	10
frequency	0	0	1	2	2	2	2	4	3	2	2

Q.	Answer	Mark	Additional Guidance
43. (i)	35	1	
(ii)	7	1	
	6 to 13	1	

Q.	Answer	Mark	Additional Guidance
(iii)	23	1	
(iv)	9	2	19 children 9 and under 16 children 10 and over so median is 9
44. (i)		4	

ages in years	tally	frequency	
7	JHT	5	
8	JHT I	6	} 12
9	I	1	
10	JHT	5	
11	III	3	
12	III	3	} 13
13	II	2	

Q.	Answer	Mark	Additional Guidance
(ii)	6 years	2	
(iii)	10 years	3	12 children aged 9 and under 13 children aged 10 and over
(iv)	8 years	1	
45. (i)		4	

pocket money	£0.00	£0.50	£1.00	£1.50	£2.00	£2.50	£3.00
number of children	1	7	18	12	4	5	3

Q.	Answer	Mark	Additional Guidance
(ii)	£1.00	2	
(iii)	three times as many children received **£1.50** as received **£2.00**	2	

Q.	Answer	Mark	Additional Guidance
46. (i)	*example:* he would need to throw a 7 so that $7 \times 2 = 14$ there is no 7 on a die	2	
(ii)		4	

scores	tally	frequency
1–6	~~IIII~~ ~~IIII~~	10
7–12	~~IIII~~	5
13–18	IIII	4
19–24	III	3
25–30	I	1
31–36	II	2
	total	25

Q.	Answer	Mark	Additional Guidance
(iii)	9	2	8 8 ⑨ 10 10 ten scores less than 7 ten scores greater than 12 so the median must be in the middle of the range 7–12

DATA A

94

Q.	Answer	Mark	Additional Guidance
(iv)		4	

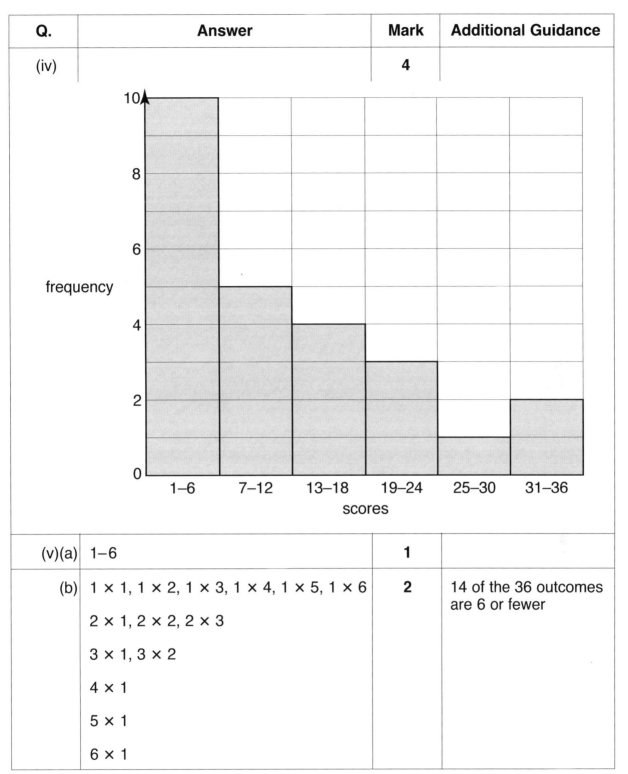

Q.	Answer	Mark	Additional Guidance
(v)(a)	1–6	1	
(b)	1×1, 1×2, 1×3, 1×4, 1×5, 1×6 2×1, 2×2, 2×3 3×1, 3×2 4×1 5×1 6×1	2	14 of the 36 outcomes are 6 or fewer

DATA A

Q.	Answer	Mark	Additional Guidance
47. (i)		4	

height (m)	tally marks	frequency
1.25 to 1.29	/	1
1.30 to 1.34	//	2
1.35 to 1.39	///	3
1.40 to 1.44	///	3
1.45 to 1.49	~~////~~/	5
1.50 to 1.54	////	4
1.55 to 1.59	/	1
total		19

Q.	Answer	Mark	Additional Guidance
(ii)		4	

Q.	Answer	Mark	Additional Guidance
(iii)	1.45 m to 1.49 m	2	
48. (i)	1	1	

Q.	Answer	Mark	Additional Guidance
(ii)	2	2	9 buy fewer than 2 11 buy more than 2 5 buy 2 so the median is 2
49. (i)		5	

number of children

amount of pocket money

Q.	Answer	Mark	Additional Guidance
(ii)	25	2	
(iii)	£7	1	
(iv)	£1	1	
50. (i)	7	1	
(ii)	7	1	
(iii)	6	1	
51. (i)	26	2	
(ii)	10	2	
(iii)	not less than 120 cm less than 130 cm	2	we cannot tell exactly

DATA A

Q.	Answer	Mark	Additional Guidance
52. (i)		4	
(ii)	12	1	
(iii)(a)	47	1	
(b)	61	1	
(iv)	11	2	using the answer (iii)(b) and the fact that 26 are aged 11
53. (i)	12	1	
(ii)	55	2	
(iii)	27 kg	2	135 ÷ 5
54. (i)	more than 80%	2	
(ii)	25	2	
(iii)	72%	2	18 out of 25
55. (i)(a)	the highest score is **48**	1	
(b)	the lowest score is **3**	1	
(c)	the range of the scores is **45**	1	

Q.	Answer	Mark	Additional Guidance
(ii)	15	4	
(iii)		5	

score	tally marks	frequency
0–9	ЖІ́ I	6
10–19	ЖІ́ IIII	9
20–29	ЖІ́ I	6
30–39	II	2
40–49	II	2
	total	25

Q.	Answer	Mark	Additional Guidance
(iv)		4	

frequency vs score

Q.	Answer	Mark	Additional Guidance
(v)	15	2	

DATA A

Q.	Answer	Mark	Additional Guidance
56. (i)		4	

mark	tally	frequency
10–19	////	4
20–29	////-/	6
30–39	////-///	8
40–49	////-//	7
50–59	//	2
60–69	//	2
70–79	/	1
	total	30

Q.	Answer	Mark	Additional Guidance
(ii)	53	2	17–70
(iii)		4	

Q.	Answer	Mark	Additional Guidance
57. (i)	180 grams	2	
(ii)	240 g	4	1200 ÷ 5
58.	4 degrees	2	⁻1 → 3 (3 − ⁻1)
59. (i)		4	

number of goals scored	tally	frequency
1–3	///	3
4–6	JHT //	7
7–9	JHT ///	8
10–12	JHT	5
13–15	//	2
	total	25

(ii) — 4

Q.	Answer	Mark	Additional Guidance
59.(iii)	7–9	1	
(iv)	7	2	in the 7–9 range … 7 7 **7** 8 8 9 9 9 … 12 scores 12 scores
(v)	7	1	
60. (i)	31.5 °C	1	
(ii)	$5\frac{1}{2}$ (5.5) degrees	1	
(iii)	29 °C	1	
(iv)	no, because temperatures recorded only at midday	2	
61. (i)	10:00	1	
(ii)	1 hour	1	
(iii)	16:00	1	
(iv)	60 km	1	
(v)	9 hours	1	
62. (i)	13:00	1	
(ii)	20 litres	1	
(iii)	15:30	1	
(iv)	35 litres	2	

DATA A

Q.	Answer	Mark	Additional Guidance
63. (i)		**3**	

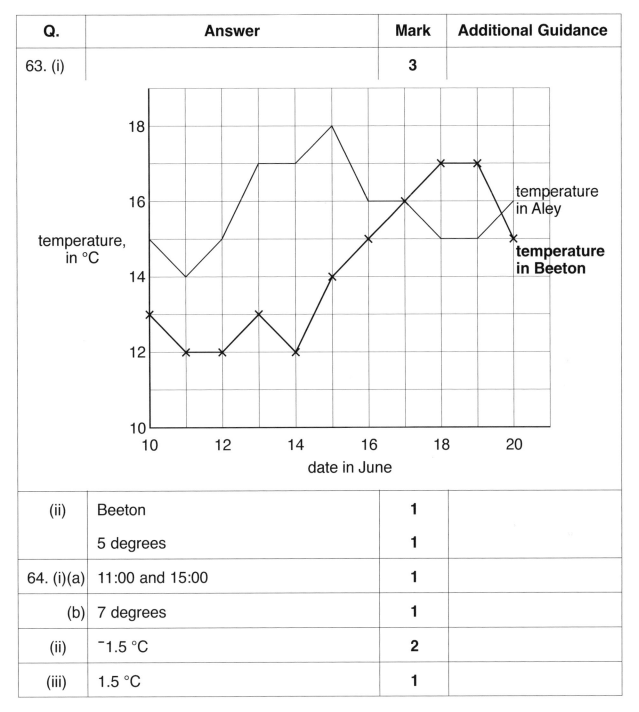

(ii)	Beeton	**1**	
	5 degrees	**1**	
64. (i)(a)	11:00 and 15:00	**1**	
(b)	7 degrees	**1**	
(ii)	⁻1.5 °C	**2**	
(iii)	1.5 °C	**1**	

DATA A

B Probability

Q.	Answer	Mark	Additional Guidance
1. (i)	no, because there are more squares than circles	2	
(ii)	yes, because there is an even chance of each outcome	2	
2. (i)	G H I J K L	2	
(ii)(a)	1 2 3 4 5 6	2	
(b)	$\frac{1}{2}$	1	
3.	<table><tr><td>red</td><td>blue</td></tr><tr><td>5</td><td>1</td></tr><tr><td>4</td><td>2</td></tr><tr><td>3</td><td>3</td></tr><tr><td>2</td><td>4</td></tr><tr><td>1</td><td>5</td></tr></table>	4	
4. (i)	<table><tr><td colspan="2">4</td></tr><tr><td>yellow</td><td>green</td></tr><tr><td>3</td><td>1</td></tr><tr><td>2</td><td>2</td></tr><tr><td>1</td><td>3</td></tr></table> <table><tr><td colspan="2">7</td></tr><tr><td>yellow</td><td>green</td></tr><tr><td>6</td><td>1</td></tr><tr><td>5</td><td>2</td></tr><tr><td>4</td><td>3</td></tr><tr><td>3</td><td>4</td></tr><tr><td>2</td><td>5</td></tr><tr><td>1</td><td>6</td></tr></table>	3	
(ii)	chances are equal	1	
5.	black black black navy black grey navy navy navy grey grey grey	6	

Q.	Answer	Mark	Additional Guidance
6. (i)	certain	1	even if we cannot see it
(ii)	certain	1	unless it falls on its edge on soft ground!
(iii)	certain	1	
(iv)	impossible	1	
7.	certain **D** very likely **A** even chance **E** not likely **C** cannot happen **B**	5	
8. (i)	unlikely	1	
(ii)	certain	1	
(iii)	even chance	1	
(iv)	very unlikely	1	
9.	**C**	2	
10. (i)	no	1	
(ii)	there is always a $\frac{1}{6}$ chance of getting each number	2	
11.		4	pupils may put their own 'divisions' on the line to help with the position of **B**

For question 11:

D   B   C   A

impossible   certain

DATA
B

105

Q.	Answer	Mark	Additional Guidance
12. (i)	impossible ——— certain	1	
(ii)	impossible ——— certain	1	
(iii)	impossible ——— certain	1	
13. (i)	poor chance	2	
(ii)	even chance	2	
(iii)	even chance	1	
(iv)	certain	2	
14.	5 times	2	
15. (i)(a)	**R**	1	
(b)	**P**	1	
(ii)(a)	$\frac{1}{4}$ $(\frac{3}{12})$	2	
(b)		2	
16. (i)		3	

score	tally	frequency
1				2
2	JHT JHT		11
3	JHT ||||	9
4	JHT JHT ||	12
5	JHT |||	8
6	JHT JHT JHT |||	18

Q.	Answer	Mark	Additional Guidance
(ii)	10	2	
(iii)	the die was biased towards 6 (and therefore against 1) *or* insufficient trials	2	
(iv)	1800	2	if a pupil has suggested 'insufficient trials' in (iii), then accept 1000 for (iv)
17. (i)	red blue 	1	2	3	4	5	6
2	4	6	8	10	12
3	6	9	12	15	18
4	8	12	16	20	24
5	10	15	20	25	30
6	12	18	24	30	36		4	
(ii)	21	2	note: four outcomes (1, 3, 3, 9) score no points!
(iii)	5	2	5, 5, 15, 15, 25
(iv)	6	2	10, 10, 20, 20, 30, 30
(v)	$\frac{1}{6}$	2	

107

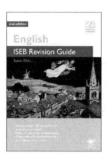

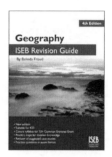

  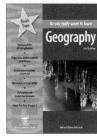  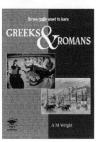